D1452167

Iki
and his
MIGHTY FRIENDS

words by
SAMANTHA GARCIA

pictures by
MARTHA JOHNSTON

ISBN: 979-8-9883933-2-0

Martha Johnston is an artist, graphic designer, and dog enthusiast. She was inspired to write Iki and his Mighty Friends about her dog-grandchild, Iki, and the Maui farm where he lives. She lives in Michigan with her husband and 3 dogs. You can find her at www.marthajohnstonart.com

Samantha Garcia is an author, digital marketer, and certified permaculture design specialist. She co-founded the non-profit Regenerative Education Centers with her husband, Eddy Garcia, in 2015. They live on their Maui farm with 3 dogs (including Iki), 7 cats, 5 salamanders, sheep, peacocks, and millions of bugs.

Regenerative Education Centers is a non-profit organization based on Maui. Our vision is to empower minds and cultivate change by sharing regenerative agriculture education and practices. With an unwavering commitment to knowledge, advocacy, and empowerment, we're creating a vibrant world for present and forthcoming generations. To learn more about our work, visit www.recenters.org.

Iki is excited to grow his first squash.

He plants the seed.

He waters it.

It grows.

OH NO!
A bug is eating my little squash.

Iki looks confused.

Worms make soil for us
to grow yummy food.

Ladybugs protect our plants
from naughty bugs.

Bees help flowers turn into fruit.

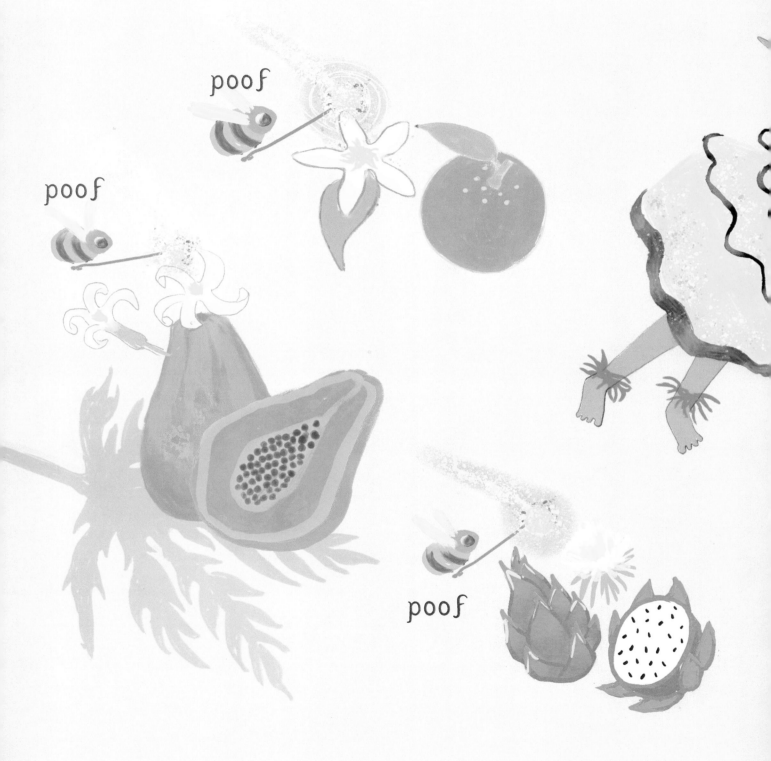

poof

poof

poof

poof

And make honey.

Roly polies chew on sticks.

And work with
our worm friends.

Printed in the USA
CPSIA information can be obtained
at www.ICGtesting.com
LVRC081340021023
759782LV00020B/187